MathLand™

Journeys Through Mathematics

Charles • Randolph Brummett • McDonald • Westley

DAILY TUNE-UPS

GRADE

K

Creative Publications®
Mountain View, CA

Art Director • JoAnne Hammer
Senior Designer • Elaine Abe

Project Editors • Ann Roper and Cynthia Reak
Production Services • The Mazer Corporation

©1995 Creative Publications
1300 Villa Street
Mountain View, California 94041

Printed in the United States of America.
ISBN: 1-56107-272-9

5 6 7 8 9 10 K 99 98 97 96

What are the Daily Tune-Ups?

The Daily Tune-Ups are 170 short, teacher-led math activities, one for each day of the typical school year.

Why are the *Daily Tune-Ups* important?

As educators become more and more influenced by the NCTM *Curriculum and Evaluation Standards for School Mathematics,* classrooms are moving toward project-based mathematics, where the children are encouraged to construct meanings for themselves through in-depth investigations, such as those found in the *MathLand Guidebook*. This is an exciting and productive way for children to learn. However, some kinds of mathematical knowledge are best learned in a different format.

The *Daily Tune-Ups* provide that other format, through short, frequent, repetitive math activities. The important skills, meanings, symbols, and terminology for each grade are collected and presented in a way that the whole class can practice together. It's quick and it's fun.

Both kinds of mathematics are extremely important, and should be included in a well-rounded mathematics program.

How do I use the *Daily Tune-Ups*?

The activities in the *Daily Tune-Ups* can be done at any time of the day: the first thing in the morning, last thing in the afternoon, just before lunch, or to start math time. Choose a time that works best for you, and make it part of your daily routine.

If you are using the *MathLand Guidebook* as your math program, remember that the *Daily Tune-Ups* are an important part of this program. They have been carefully sequenced to introduce the knowledge necessary for the activity units and to reinforce skills following the units. You can choose the time of day, but don't skip your *Daily Tune-Ups*; they're essential!

Tune-Ups Tips

- Expand the Tune-Ups with examples of your own.

- Allow the children to "be the teacher" for some of the Tune-Ups.

- Copy some of the Tune-Ups and send them home to help reinforce skills.

- If a Tune-Up seems too difficult for most of your children, mark it and come back to it later in the year.

- If a Tune-Up seems too difficult for some of your children, work with them separately at another time.

- Use the Tune-Ups as mini-assessments, taking one or more children aside to try the activity. Carefully observe their responses.

- Keep a list of the Tune-Ups your class really thinks are fun and repeat these!

- Show off your class's Tune-Ups skills to classroom visitors.

- The idea of wait time is important when doing the Tune-Ups. Children need adequate time (at least 3 seconds) to reflect before responding. Teach the class a signal, such as a finger snap, a hand clap, or the word *now*. Wait long enough for everyone to respond.

How are the *Daily Tune-Ups* organized?

The Grade Kindergarten *Daily Tune-Ups* involve twelve content topics:

Patterns	Auditory memory
Counting	Mental math
Number recognition	Number stories
Sequencing numbers	Estimation
Measurement	Visual memory
Geometry	Logical thinking

These topics are used repeatedly throughout the year, each time with a slightly different focus. In the beginning, the counting focus is on numbers 1 to 10. Later the counting focus is on numbers beyond 10.

How do I integrate the *Daily Tune-Ups* into my mathematics curriculum?

If you are using the *MathLand Guidebook*, the *Daily Tune-Ups* are sequenced and coordinated to match the organization of the weeks in the *MathLand Guidebook*. You simply use the *Daily Tune-Ups* listed at the beginning of each unit.

If you are using another mathematics program, the *Daily Tune-Ups* can enhance it. Because the Tune-Ups deal with common mathematical topics, you can easily fit them into your program. The chart on pages T7-T15 will help you select the *Daily Tune-Ups* appropriate to the topic you are teaching.

Daily Tune-Ups Materials

If you are using the MathLand Guidebook, most of the materials listed below can be found in the Classroom Kit and the Consumable Kit. If you are not using the MathLand Guidebook, the Daily Tune-Ups Kit includes these materials.

Other materials can be easily collected from home or prepared by the teacher in advance.

Manipulative Materials

LinkerCubes™

Teddy Bear Counters

Tactile Number Tiles

Treasures: buttons, creepy crawlers, tiles, nuts and washers

Pattern Blocks

Consumable Materials

Miniboards

Other Materials

Empty juice can

Empty plastic container large enough to hold 100 Teddy Bear Counters

Various shapes cut from construction paper so that two or three of the shapes fit at a time on the overhead projector stage: square, triangle, circle, rectangle, star, and heart.

Daily Tune-Ups

Activity	Topic	Focus
1 Count and Clap	Counting	Rote counting to 3
2 Count and Clap	Counting	Rote counting to 5
3 Copy Cats	Number recognition	Naming numbers 1 to 10
4 Number Flash	Number recognition	Naming numbers 1 to 10
5 Who Can Count?	Counting	Rote counting 1 to 10
6 Copy Cats	Patterns	Following motion patterns
7 Clap and Pat	Counting	Rote counting in patterns
8 Speed It Up	Counting	Rote counting to 6
9 Write It Down!	Number recognition	Writing numerals
10 Let's Move!	Patterns	Following motion patterns
11 Count and Do	Counting	Rote counting in patterns
12 Write It Down!	Number recognition	Writing numerals
13 Perk Up Your Ears	Patterns	Following sound patterns
14 Faster and Faster	Number recognition	Naming numbers 1 to 10
15 Let's Move!	Patterns	Following motion patterns

Activity	Topic	Focus
16 Memory Test	Visual memory	Remembering displayed numbers
17 Color Reading	Patterns	Interpreting visual patterns verbally
18 Was That All Right?	Sequencing numbers	Listening for missing numbers in a sequence
19 Count and Grow	Counting	Rote counting 1 to 10
20 Nod Your Head	Number recognition	Identifying numbers 1 to 10
21 Up to Ten	Counting	Rote counting in patterns
22 Count and Clap	Counting	Rote counting from numbers other than 1
23 Numbers in the Air	Number recognition	Writing numerals
24 Back Patterns	Patterns	Following motion patterns
25 A Dot and a Box	Auditory memory	Following directions
26 Stand and Sit	Counting	Rote counting in patterns
27 Who Can Count?	Counting	Rote counting to 10
28 Memory Test	Visual memory	Remembering displayed numbers
29 Speed It Up!	Counting	Rote counting to 10
30 What's Missing?	Sequencing numbers	Naming missing numbers in a sequence
31 Show Me	Counting	Showing numbers with objects
32 Draw It!	Auditory memory	Following directions
33 Shape Hunt	Geometry	Identifying shapes around you
34 Knees and Toes	Counting	Rote counting in patterns
35 One After the Other	Patterns	Following motion patterns

Activity	Topic	Focus
36 Count with Me	Counting	Rote counting in patterns
37 Write It Down	Number recognition	Writing numerals
38 Five Little Monkeys	Auditory memory	Repeating number rhymes
39 Blast Off!	Counting	Rote counting backward
40 Numbers on the Back	Number recognition	Writing numerals
41 Shapes in a Row	Patterns	Identifying the next element in a pattern
42 Four by Four	Counting	Counting with 1-to-1 correspondence
43 Let's Count!	Counting	Rote counting 1 to 10
44 Say It and Write It	Number recognition	Naming numbers 1 to 10
45 What's Next?	Patterns	Identifying the next element in a pattern
46 Let's Move!	Counting	Rote counting with movements
47 Up to Nine	Counting	Rote counting from numbers other than 1
48 Quick Peeks	Counting	Instant recognition of sets to 5
49 Is This Right?	Patterns	Identifying the next element in a pattern
50 Bees in the Hive	Auditory memory	Repeating number rhymes
51 Yes/No	Counting	Instant recognition of sets to 5
52 Countdowns	Counting	Rote counting backwards
53 Riddle Time	Logical thinking	Identifying objects given clues
54 Catch Me if You Can	Sequencing numbers	Listening for mistakes in number sequences
55 In Common	Logical thinking	Naming common attributes

Activity	Topic	Focus
56 Listen and Count	Counting	Counting with 1-to-1 correspondence
57 Speed It Up	Counting	Rote counting to 10
58 Faster and Faster	Number recognition	Naming numbers 1 to 10
59 Clap and Count	Counting	Rote counting in patterns
60 How Is It the Same?	Logical thinking	Naming objects with shared attributes
61 Animal Sounds	Counting	Instant recognition of sets to 5
62 Memory Test	Visual memory	Remembering displayed objects
63 One, Two	Counting	Learning a counting rhyme
64 Three Bears Counting	Counting	Rote counting to 10
65 In Your Best Writing	Number recognition	Writing numerals
66 Hugs and Kisses	Patterns	Identifying the next element in a pattern
67 Yes/No	Number recognition	Locating a number
68 Blast Off!	Counting	Rote counting backward
69 Plop, Plop	Counting	Rote counting 1 to 10
70 Numbers on the Back	Number recognition	Writing numerals
71 Speed It Up!	Number recognition	Naming numbers 1 to 10
72 Say It Fast	Number recognition	Naming numbers 1 to 10
73 Quick Peeks	Counting	Instant recognition of sets to 5
74 Draw This	Counting	Counting with 1-to-1 correspondence
75 Count to Ten	Counting	Rote counting 1 to 10

Activity	Topic	Focus
76 Count My Claps	Counting	Counting with 1-to-1 correspondence
77 Make a List	Number recognition	Writing numerals
78 Shape Escape	Visual memory	Identifying missing items
79 Point It Out!	Number recognition	Identifying numbers 1 to 10
80 Take a Turn	Counting	Rote counting 1 to 10
81 If It's True…	Logical thinking	Identifying true and false statements
82 Name That Number	Number recognition	Naming numbers 1 to 10
83 Long Sleeves, Short Sleeves	Counting	Counting with 1-to-1 correspondence
84 Yes/No	Number recognition	Locating numbers in a group
85 Treasure Count	Counting	Counting with 1-to-1 correspondence
86 Number Detective	Number recognition	Naming numbers 1 to 10
87 Fast Fingers	Counting	Instant recognition of sets to 5
88 Plop, Plop	Counting	Rote counting to 10
89 I Spy	Logical thinking	Identifying objects given clues
90 If It's True…	Logical thinking	Identifying true and false statements
91 Riddles	Logical thinking	Identifying objects given clues
92 I Can't Hear You…	Counting	Rote counting 1 to 10
93 Show Me	Number recognition	Writing numerals
94 Sound Patterns	Patterns	Following sound patterns
95 What Comes Next?	Patterns	Identifying the next element in a pattern

Activity	Topic	Focus
96 Top, Middle, or Bottom?	Number recognition	Locating a number among others
97 What's Next?	Sequencing numbers	Naming the next number
98 On Beyond Ten	Counting	Rote counting beyond 10
99 Write It Down!	Number recognition	Writing numerals
100 Hungry Bug	Number stories	Gathering data from a story
101 Picnic Lunch	Number stories	Gathering data from a story
102 Who Can Count?	Counting	Rote counting beyond 10
103 Clap and Count	Counting	Counting with 1-to-1 correspondence
104 Riddle Me This	Logical thinking	Identifying objects given clues
105 On Beyond 10	Counting	Rote counting beyond 10
106 Number Noises	Counting	Counting with 1-to-1 correspondence
107 Make a Mark	Number stories	Gathering data from a story
108 Listen and Count	Counting	Counting with 1-to-1 correspondence
109 Quick Peeks	Visual memory	Remembering displayed numbers
110 Clap and Count	Counting	Counting on silently
111 A Fish Story	Number stories	Gathering data from a story
112 Plop, Plop	Counting	Rote counting beyond 10
113 Faster and Faster	Number recognition	Naming numbers 1 to 10
114 Write a Number…	Sequencing numbers	Naming numbers greater than/less than
115 How Many?	Counting	Counting with 1-to-1 correspondence

Activity	Topic	Focus
116 Echoes	Auditory memory	Repeating a series of sounds
117 Write It Down!	Number recognition	Writing numerals
118 Count On	Counting	Counting on
119 Estimate	Estimation	Estimation of groups of 5 to 10 objects
120 Listen and Count	Counting	Counting with 1-to-1 correspondence
121 Name My Shape	Geometry	Naming shapes
122 Number Detective	Sequencing numbers	Identifying a number given clues
123 Count On	Counting	Counting on
124 How High?	Counting	Rote counting 1 to 100
125 Monster Story	Number stories	Gathering data from a story
126 Alike and Different	Logical thinking	Identifying common attributes
127 Draw This	Geometry	Drawing shapes
128 Zoo Stories	Number stories	Gathering data from a story
129 Count 'Em Up	Mental math	Visualizing numbers
130 Fifty Is Nifty	Counting	Rote counting to 50
131 Let's Estimate!	Visual memory	Making estimates
132 It Was a Mess!	Number stories	Gathering data from a story
133 Let's Count!	Counting	Rote counting 1 to 100
134 Draw This	Geometry	Drawing shapes
135 What Comes Next?	Sequencing numbers	Writing the next number

Activity	Topic	Focus
136 Sizing Up	Measurement	Size comparisons
137 Your Best Writing	Number recognition	Writing numerals
138 Yes/No	Geometry	Identifying shapes
139 Whisper, SHOUT	Counting	Skip counting by twos
140 Memory Test	Auditory memory	Re-creating a list of numbers
141 Number Riddles	Sequencing numbers	Identifying numbers given clues
142 Draw This	Measurement	Size comparisons
143 Count On	Counting	Counting on
144 What Comes Before?	Sequencing numbers	Naming the previous number
145 Lengthy Lines	Measurement	Comparing lengths
146 Who Can Count?	Counting	Rote counting beyond 10
147 Show Me	Number recognition	Writing numerals
148 Point It Out	Measurement	Identifying longer, shorter
149 Write a Number…	Sequencing numbers	Greater than/less than
150 What's My Number?	Sequencing numbers	Identifying numbers given clues
151 Count 'Em Up	Mental math	Visualizing numbers
152 100 Count	Counting	Rote counting 1 to 100
153 Two by Two	Counting	Skip counting by twos
154 What's Next?	Sequencing numbers	Naming the next number
155 Plop, Plop	Counting	Rote counting 1 to 100

Activity	Topic	Focus
156 Listen Closely!	Auditory memory	Following directions
157 Count 'Em Up	Number recognition	Locating a number among others
158 Bigger and Smaller	Measurement	Comparing size
159 Countdown	Counting	Rote counting backwards
160 Memory Test	Visual memory	Remembering displayed numbers
161 Clap and Count	Counting	Rote counting 1 to 100
162 Counting Back	Counting	Rote counting backwards
163 Yes/No	Counting	Instant recognition of sets to 5
164 On the Nose	Sequencing numbers	Comparing numbers 1 to 10
165 Write Two Numbers...	Sequencing numbers	Greater than/less than
166 Start at Twenty	Counting	Rote counting 1 to 100
167 Which Is More?	Sequencing numbers	Identifying which is greater
168 Which Is Less?	Sequencing numbers	Identifying which is less
169 What Comes Next?	Sequencing numbers	Naming the next number
170 Count and Kick	Counting	Rote counting 1 to 100

◇ 1 ◇ Count and Clap

Here's a counting and clapping pattern. Join in when you've caught on.

1, 2, 3, clap, clap, clap; *1, 2, 3,* clap, clap, clap; …

Try these:

- *1,* clap, clap, clap, *2, 3; 1,* clap, clap, clap, *2, 3;* …

- *1, 2,* clap, clap, *3; 1, 2,* clap, clap, *3;* …

- *1,* clap, *2,* clap, *3,* clap; *1,* clap, *2,* clap, *3,* clap; …

What's another counting and clapping pattern for 3?

Count and Clap

Let's count and clap. Listen closely and join in when you know the pattern.

Try these:

- *1, 2, 3, 4, 5,* clap, clap; *1, 2, 3, 4, 5,* clap, clap; …
- *1, 2, 3,* clap, clap, *4, 5; 1, 2, 3,* clap, clap, *4, 5;* …
- *1, 2,* clap, clap, *3, 4, 5; 1, 2,* clap, clap, *3, 4, 5;* …

Can anyone think of another pattern for 5?

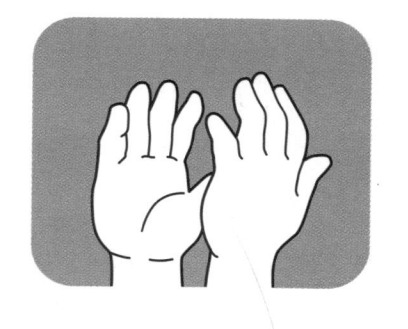

3 Copy Cats

On the overhead projector, write three numbers from 1 to 10.
I wrote three numbers on the overhead projector. Look at them and copy them onto your Miniboard.

Show me your boards. Can you point to the 3? Can you point to the 5? What's the other number on your board?

Now let's try three new numbers.

Number Flash

I'll flash a number on the overhead projector. Say the number as soon as you know it.

Using the overhead projector, write one number at a time from 1 to 10. Turn the light on very briefly to reveal the number to the children. Try a variety of numbers from 1 to 10. Continue as time permits.

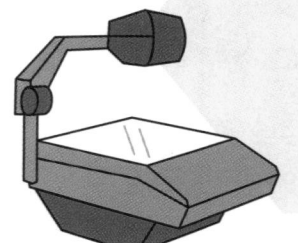

5 ◆ Who Can Count?

Who can count to 10? Would you show us?

Call on individuals to count to 10 for the group.

Now let's all count to 10 together.

1, 2, 3, … 10!

6 Copy Cats

Watch my hands and copy what I do. Try a variety of motion patterns. Keep each pattern going until most of the children are confident with it.

Try these:

• Clap, pat your knees; clap, pat your knees; …

• Touch head, touch shoulders; touch head, touch shoulders; …

• Arms up, arms down; arms up, arms down; …

Clap and Pat

Count with me and follow what I do. We'll clap five times, then pat our knees five times. Count in loud voices during the claps, and count softly during the pats. Start the clap, pat pattern, counting along in rhythm.

Try these:

- CLAP, CLAP, CLAP, CLAP, CLAP.
  ONE, TWO, THREE, FOUR, FIVE.

- Pat, pat, pat, pat, pat.
  One, two, three, four, five.

Repeat each pattern over and over, until the class counts and moves confidently. Then count and clap to a new number, such as 8.

Speed It Up

8

Let's count to 6. We'll think of different ways to do it each time. Count from 1 to 6, doing something different each time you repeat the sequence.

Try these:

• *Let's count to 6 s-l-o-w-l-y. Count with me: 1, 2, 3, 4, 5, 6.*

• *Now let's count a little faster.*

• *Now let's count really fast!*

9   Write It Down!

I'll say a number. I'd like for you to write it on your Miniboard. Ready?

In turn, say several numbers from 1 to 10, having the children write each one on their board and show it to you.

10 Let's Move!

Let's make some patterns by moving our bodies.
Watch me, and join in when you know the pattern.

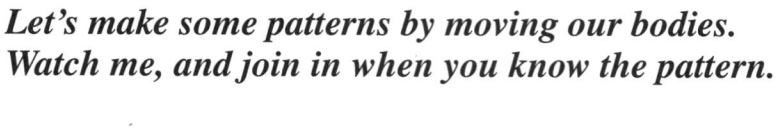

Try these:

• Hop, hop, hop, crouch; hop, hop, hop, crouch; …

• Crouch, jump up, jump up; crouch, jump up, jump up; …

• Step forward, jump back; step forward, jump back; …

11 Count and Do

Let's bend from one side to the other as we count to 2 again and again.

1 (bend left), *2* (bend right); *1* (bend left), *2* (bend right); …

Now let's count to 3 over and over again. Join me when you know the body motions.

1 (tap knees), *2* (clap), *3* (touch shoulders); *1* (tap knees), *2* (clap), *3* (touch shoulders); …

Can anyone lead us in a new counting and moving pattern?

Write It Down!

I'm going to say two numbers from 1 to 10. Write them on your Miniboard. Show me your board. Good. Now clear your boards and I'll say two different numbers.

Use numbers from 1 to 10. Try this activity several times.

13 Perk Up Your Ears

How good are your ears? Listen to my pattern and join in when you can.

Try these:

Shhh, bzzz, shhh, bzzz.

- Stamp, clap, clap; stamp, clap, clap; …

- *Shhh, bzzz; shhh, bzzz; …*

- *Woof, woof, meow, meow; woof, woof, meow, meow; …*

Have the children help you think of some more patterns!

Write three numbers from 1 to 10 on the chalkboard.

Here are three numbers. When I point to each number, say it out loud. Watch out, if I think you're really good at this I might try to go faster!

Continue pointing to the numbers in random order. When the children feel confident with the number names, begin pointing from one to the other faster and faster.

Try three different numbers from 1 to 10.

15 Let's Move!

Copy what I do. Join in when you know what to do.

Try these:

• Head left, head right, head back;
  head left, head right, head back; …

• Tug ears, tug ears, touch nose;
  tug ears, tug ears, touch nose; …

• Tap head, tap knees, tap knees;
  tap head, tap knees, tap knees; …

I'll turn on the overhead projector for just a second. On it, you'll see two numbers. Try to remember them and write them on your Miniboard.

Use numbers from 1 to 10. Turn the overhead light on briefly, then turn it off and have the children write the numbers they remember seeing.

Let's try two different numbers!

4

7

⟨17⟩ Color Reading

Make a linear pattern of red and blue dots on an overhead transparency. Display the pattern on the overhead projector.

Let's read this pattern. Say each color as I point to the dots.

Point to each dot in the line, as the children "read" the colors to you chorally.

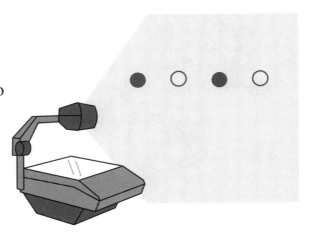

Try these:

- Ⓡ Ⓑ Ⓡ Ⓑ
- Ⓡ Ⓑ Ⓑ Ⓡ Ⓑ Ⓑ
- Ⓡ Ⓡ Ⓑ Ⓑ Ⓡ Ⓡ Ⓑ Ⓑ

Topic: Patterns **Focus:** Interpreting visual patterns verbally

MathLand™: Grade Kindergarten
© Creative Publications

Was That All Right?

I'm going to count to 6. Listen to make sure I do it right. 1, 2, 3, 4, 5, 6. Was that all right? Now listen again. 1, 2, 4, 5, 6. Did I do it right?

Count several times, eliminating the same number, then choose a new number, such as 9.

No! You missed the 3!

19   Count and Grow

Count to 7 over and over with the children. Have them use their bodies as they count.

Let's count to 7 again and again. Start in a crouch. As we count up, stand up taller and taller. When we get to 7, you should be standing tall. Then go back to a crouch to start the count again.

Try "Count and Grow" with some other numbers from 1 to 10.

Nod Your Head

Write four numbers from 1 to 10 on the chalkboard.

I'll ask you some questions. Nod your head "yes" or "no" to answer. Is there a 7 on the board? Is there a 5? How about a 9 on the board?

Now let's try it again with some different numbers.

21 Up to Ten

Let's count to 10. We'll start at some different numbers and go from there to 10. Ready?

Try these:

- *Let's count to 10 starting at 1.*  *1, 2, 3, … 10.*

- *Let's count to 10 starting with 3.*  *3, 4, 5, … 10.*

- *How about starting at 5?*  *5, 6, 7, … 10.*

- *Once more! Let's start with 9.*  *9, 10.*

Listen to my pattern. Then we'll do it together.

Start a slow pattern. Alternate between clapping and patting your knees. Keep the counting pattern going until the children are very confident with it.

Count and clap with me when you know the pattern.

Try these:

- *1* (clap), *2* (pat); *1* (clap), *2* (pat); …

- *1* (pat), *2* (clap), *3* (clap); *1* (pat), *2* (clap), *3* (clap); …

- *1* (pat), *2* (pat), *3* (clap), *4* (clap); *1* (pat), *2* (pat), *3* (clap), *4* (clap); …

23 ◇ Numbers in the Air

I'm going to say a number. I'd like you to draw its shape in the air.

Try a variety of numbers from 1 to 9.

Back Patterns

Have the children pair up. One partner should have his back to the other. *Let's try some back-patting patterns. I'll start. Join in when you can do the pattern on your partner's back.*

Pat your knee to indicate the pattern. Children may join in as they feel comfortable.

Try these:

• Long, short, short; long, short, short; …

• Short, short, short, long; short, short, short, long; …

• Tap, tap, pat, pat; tap, tap, pat, pat; …

A Dot and a Box

Have the children get out their Miniboards. Draw a dot and a square on a Miniboard. Show it to the class. ***Here's a dot and here's a box.***

Try these:

• ***Draw a dot inside of a box. Show me.***

• ***Now draw a dot on top of a box. Let's see how that looks.***

• ***How about a dot beside a box? Let's see.***

Have the children show you their Miniboards after each direction. Before each new instruction, have the children clear their boards.

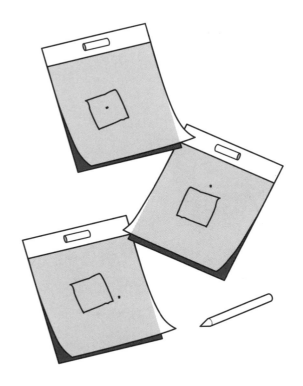

Topic: Auditory memory   **Focus:** Following directions   MathLand™: Grade Kindergarten
© Creative Publications

Let's count to 10. Try it this way. First we'll count to 10 standing up, then we'll sit down and count to 10.

Keep up the pattern: stand and count to 10, sit and count to 10, stand and count to 10, sit and count to 10....

1, 2, 3... 10.

27 Who Can Count?

Who can count to 7? Show us. Have several children share their counting. **Now let's all do it together.**

Repeat the activity with other numbers from 1 to 10 as time permits.

1, 2, 3… 7!

Memory Test

I'll turn on the overhead projector for just a second. On it, you'll see two numbers. Try to remember them and write them on your Miniboard.

Use numbers from 1 to 10. Turn the overhead light on briefly, then turn it off and have the children write the numbers they remember seeing.

Now let's try three numbers.

Speed It Up

Let's count to 8 over and over. Each time we count, we'll speed it up just a bit. Try to stay together!

Now let's try counting to 9 again and again. Follow me. Try to stay together.

What's Missing?

I'll count for you, but I'll leave out a number. See if you can tell what number I left out. Listen closely, I'll count slowly.

Try these:

- *1, 2, 3, 5, 6, 7...What got left out?*

- *4, 5, 7, 8, 9 ...What got left out?*

- *2, 3, 5, 6, 7...What got left out?*

31 ◇ Show Me

Have the children hold up fingers to show various numbers that you call out.

Try these:

• *Show me 3.*

• *Show me 5.*

• *Show me 2.*

Let's see if you can show me 4, but use some fingers from both hands!

Draw It!

**Today is a Miniboard day! Listen carefully now and do what
I say.** Have the children use their Miniboards as you tell them
what to draw. Be sure to allow time for the children to clear
their Miniboards after each direction.

Try these:

• **Draw a medium-sized square.**

• **Now draw a triangle with a square inside it.**

• **Try to draw a circle with a square next to it.**

33 Shape Hunt

Look around the room. Can you find something that's the shape of a circle? Put your finger on your nose when you find something. Let's hear about some of the things you spotted.

Have the children look for squares and triangles around the room, too.

Knees and Toes

Let's count together as we touch our head, shoulders, knees, and toes. Count in unison, touching heads on 1, shoulders on 2, knees on 3, and toes on 4…. *Let's try to keep this pattern going.*

Now let's try to speed it up a bit. Follow me!

35 ◆ One After the Other

Let's do a pattern. I'll pick two movements, and we'll do them one after the other. Let's keep the pattern going for a while. Try to stay together!

Pick different motions to put together, always using an AB pattern structure.

Try these:

- Arms at sides, arms crossed; arms at sides, arms crossed; …

- Head left, head right; head left, head right; …

- Pat knees, clap; pat knees, clap; …

Count with Me

Count with me as we pat our knees and clap our hands.

1 (pat), *2* (clap), *3* (pat), *4* (clap), ... *9* (pat), *10* (clap).

Continue the pattern, counting to 10 again and again.

37 Write It Down!

Are your Miniboards ready? I'll say a number. I'd like for you to write it on your Miniboard.

Have children show you their boards after each number. Try several numbers from 1 to 10.

Five Little Monkeys

Here's a little finger play. Say it with me. You can act it out as if your fingers are the monkeys.

Five little monkeys jumping on the bed.
One fell out and he bumped his head.
Mama called the doctor, and the doctor said,
"No more monkeys jumping on the bed!"

Four little monkeys jumping on the bed...

39 ◇ Blast Off!

Let's play "Blast Off." Ready? Count down from 5 with me. When we get to 1, say BLAST OFF! and jump up high!

Play "Blast Off" with other numbers. Start counting back from 7 or 9, for instance.

Topic: Counting

Focus: Rote count

Numbers on the Back

Have the children pair off, one partner sitting with her back to the other. *I'll say a number. Use your finger to draw the number on your partner's back.* Say different numbers from 1 to 10.

The children can take turns being the one to draw the numbers.

41 Shapes in a Row

Draw a linear shape pattern on the chalkboard.

Here's a shape pattern. What comes next? Draw that shape on your Miniboard.

Try these:

• △ □ △ □ △ ?

• ○ ○ □ ○ ○ ?

• △ △ ○ ○ △ △ ○ ?

Four by Four

Using the Treasures on the overhead projector, display a group of 4 buttons, a group of 4 creepy crawlers, and a group of 4 tiles.

Try these:

• *Let's count the creepies. 1, 2, 3, 4.*

• *How about the buttons? 1, 2, 3, 4.*

• *Now let's count the tiles. 1, 2, 3, 4.*

Try the activity again, making the sets represent other numbers from 1 to 10.

Let's Count!

Let's count to 7. First let's do it in whispery voices. Now let's try it in low, gruff voices. One more time. Let's use high, squeaky voices.

Does anyone have a different kind of voice we can use to count to 7?

1, 2, 3... 7!

Say It and Write It

On the chalkboard, write five or six numbers from 1 to 10.

As I point to each number, say it and write it on your Miniboard. Ready?

What's Next?

Draw a linear pattern (triangle, triangle, square, triangle, triangle) on the chalkboard.

What do you think comes next in the pattern? Draw the shape on your Miniboard.

Try a few other simple shape patterns.

Let's Move!

Let's give our muscles a little workout. We'll do each movement 6 times. Count out loud as you move!

First, jumping jacks: 1, 2, 3, 4, 5, 6.

Now, touch your toes: 1, 2, 3, 4, 5, 6.

Stretch up tall: 1, 2, 3, 4, 5, 6.

Hop on one foot: 1, 2, 3, 4, 5, 6.

Bend your knees: 1, 2, 3, 4, 5, 6.

47 ◆ Up to Nine

Have the children count with you up to 9. Each time, start with a different number.

Ready? Let's count to 9 starting with 1. Now let's count to 9 starting with 4. How about starting at 5? Do any of you have a number you want to start with? We'll count to 9 from there.

1, 2, 3, ... 9.

Quick Peeks

Use a small group of Treasures (1 to 5) and place them on the overhead projector stage.

There are some Treasures on the overhead projector. I'll show them to you for just a few seconds. When the light goes off, tell me how many you saw.

Turn on the light for just a few seconds. Have the children respond chorally, saying how many Treasures they counted.

Play the game several times, putting groups of 1 to 5 Treasures on the projector stage.

Topic: Counting   **Focus:** Instant recognition of sets to 5

49 ◆ Is This Right?

Put a line of Pattern Blocks on the overhead projector and show
them to the children.

*I'll add a block to the pattern. Sign for "yes" if it continues
the pattern correctly. Sign for "no" if it's not the block that
comes next.*

Try these:

*American Sign Language (ASL) signs
for Yes (top) and No (bottom).

Let's try this finger play.

Here is the beehive. (Show your fist).
Where are the bees?
Hiding away where nobody sees.

Watch them come creeping out of the hive.
1, 2, 3, 4, 5. (Put up a finger for each number).
Bzzzzz. (Show fingers wiggling).

◇ 51 ◇ Yes/No

Play the Yes/No game. Arrange three small groups of Treasures (1 to 5) on the overhead projector.

When the overhead light comes on, look at the groups of Treasures. Does each group show the same number of Treasures? Sign "yes" if they do; sign "no" if they don't.

Play several rounds of the Yes/No game, using numbers from 1 to 5.

*American Sign Language (ASL) signs for Yes (top) and No (bottom).

Countdown

Have the children count back with you, starting at different numbers from 2 to 10. As they count back, they should stoop lower and lower, until the number 1 is reached. Then you say, "Pop!" and the children spring back up for the next countdown.

Try these:

• *Let's count down from 5.*   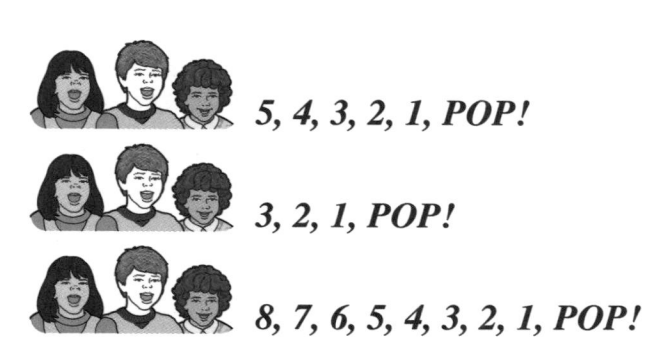   *5, 4, 3, 2, 1, POP!*

• *Let's count down from 3.*   *3, 2, 1, POP!*

• *Let's count down from 8.*   *8, 7, 6, 5, 4, 3, 2, 1, POP!*

◆ 53 ◆ **Riddle Time**

*Here are some riddles for you. Raise your hand when you
know the answer.*

*What has black and white stripes,
moves on 4 legs,
and looks a bit like a horse?* (a zebra)

*What's gray and never goes
anywhere without its trunk?* (an elephant)

*What has 8 legs,
hides in corners
and is good at spinning
and weaving?* (a spider)

Topic: Logical thinking　　　　　　　**Focus:** Identifying objects given clues　　　MathLand™: Grade Kindergarten
© Creative Publications

Catch Me if You Can...

I'll count for you, but I won't always start at 1. Keep your ears open for any mistakes I make. Put your hand up as soon as you hear a mistake. Clap for me if I finish without making a mistake.

3, 4 , 5, 7, 8, 9, 19.

Try these:

• *1, 2, 3, 4, 5.*

• *3, 4, 5, 7, 8, 9, 19.*

• *1, 2, 3, 4, 5, 4, 5, 6, 7, 8.*

55 ◆ In Common

I'll name three things. Tell me what they have in common.

List several things and let the children share all of their ideas about how the things are alike.

Try these:

• *Car, bus, and a wagon*

• *Bird, airplane, and a mosquito*

• *Dog, gerbil, and a cat*

They all have fur.

They can all be pets.

Topic: Logical thinking   **Focus:** Naming common attributes

I'll stamp my foot. Count the stamps and write how many on your Miniboard.

Stamp your foot, using numbers from 1 to 10. Repeat the activity several times.

⬦ 57 ⬦ Speed It Up

Let's count to 9. We'll think of different ways to do it each time. Count from 1 to 9, doing something different each time you repeat the sequence.

Try these:

- *Let's count to 9 s-l-o-w-l-y.*

- *Now let's count a little faster.*

- *Now let's count really fast!*

Repeat this using other numbers up to 10.

Faster and Faster

Write three numbers from 1 to 10 on the chalkboard.

Here are three numbers. When I point to each number, say it out loud. Watch out, I might start to go faster!

Point to the numbers in random order. When the children are confident with the number names, begin pointing from one to the other faster and faster.

◇ 59 ◇ Clap and Count

Let's count to 4. Now let's count to 4 and clap as we say each number. Ready?

Now let's put the two together to make a pattern. Count to 4 with claps, then count to 4 without claps.

Keep the counting pattern going a while, then introduce a new counting pattern.

How Is It the Same?

Name an object. Call on volunteers to name something that's like your object in some way.

Who can name something that's like a dog in some way? What is it? How is it like a dog?

Who can name something different that's like a dog in some way? What is it? How is it like a dog?

Let a number of children share their thoughts and reasons. Then play again, using a different object. Some examples are a bike, Jello, worms, a tree, and a pencil.

A cat is like a dog because of course they both have 4 feet.

61 Animal Sounds

Choose an animal (cow, duck, dog, pig) sound to imitate.

I'll hold up some fingers. *You make the animal sound that many times.*

Use from 1 to 5 fingers. Keep the action moving at a good pace. Each time the children finish a round, immediately change the number of fingers. The goal here is quick recognition of groups of 1 to 5. Periodically change the animal noises.

I'll turn on the overhead projector for just a second. On the screen, you'll see three numbers. Try to remember all of them and write them on your Miniboard.

Use numbers from 1 to 10. Turn the overhead light on briefly, then turn it off and have the children write the numbers they remember seeing.

Okay. Now let's try three different numbers!

One, Two

Teach the children this simple counting rhyme and say it together. Have the children hold up fingers to match the numbers they hear.

1, 2, buckle my shoe.

3, 4, shut the door.

5, 6, pick up sticks.

7, 8, lay them straight.

9, 10, a big fat hen.

Three Bears Counting

Let's count to 9. Can you count in different voices? Let's count like the Three Bears. Count to 9 like Papa Bear. Can you count like Mama Bear? Now let's count to 9 in Baby Bear's voice.

Count to different numbers up to 10, using a different bear voice each time.

65 In Your Best Writing

Get out your Miniboards! I'll give you a number. Write it on your Miniboard three times. Use your very best writing. Then we'll all show our boards.

Give the children numbers from 1 to 10. Have them write each numeral three times on their Miniboards. After they've shown their boards, have the children clear them in preparation for your next number.

Hugs and Kisses

Ready? Here's the secret code for a kiss. Draw an *X* on the chalkboard. *Here's the code for a hug.* Draw an *O* on the chalkboard. *I'll draw some kisses and hugs patterns. You try to predict what comes next. Write it on your Miniboard.*

Draw one pattern at a time. Let the children "read" the pattern chorally with you and then draw what comes next.

Try these:

Kiss, hug, hug.
Kiss, hug, hug . . .

• X O O X O O ...

• O O X X O O X ...

• X X X O X X X ...

Topic: Patterns   **Focus:** Identifying the next element in a pattern

Yes/No

On the overhead projector, write these four numbers: 8, 4, 7, and 1.

Look at these numbers. I'll say some numbers. Sign for "yes" if the number is on my list. Sign for "no" if it's not. Is there a 7? How about a 3? Do you see an 8? What about a 1?

Repeat the activity several times, each time changing the list of numbers on the screen. Vary the questions so that the children get a chance to answer both "yes" and "no".

*American Sign Language (ASL) signs for Yes (top) and No (bottom).

Blast Off!

Ready? Let's count back from 10 to 1. At the end, we'll say "BLAST OFF!"

Count back from other numbers less than 10, "blasting off" at the end of each sequence.

69 Plop, Plop

Show the children a handful of Teddy Bear Counters and an empty juice can.

I'll drop some teddy bears into the container. Count with me as each one "plops" into the can. Whenever I raise my hand, it means to start over at 1 on the next teddy bear.

Drop the teddy bears slowly into the can. Each time the count reaches 5, raise your hand for the children to start back at 1 when the next teddy bear drops.

Empty the can and try the activity again. Raise your hand after a different number each time.

Topic: Counting   **Focus:** Rote counting 1 to 10

MathLand™: Grade Kindergarten
© Creative Publications

Numbers on the Back

Have the children pair up. One partner should have his back to the other.

Use your finger to write each of the numbers from 1 to 10 on your partner's back. When you get done, switch places so that your partner can write the numbers.

71 Speed It Up

Write these numbers on the overhead projector: 9, 4, 6, and 2.

I'll point to a number. You say its name. Look out! I'll speed it up after a bit.

Point to one number at a time, in random order. When it seems that the children are confident, step up the pace.

Try the activity with several lists of numbers from 1 to 10.

9 4
6 2

Say It Fast

Hold up one Tactile Number Tile.

I'll hold up a number tile. Look at it and say the number as fast as you can.

Try the activity a number of times, moving quickly from one number tile to the next.

4

Quick Peeks

I'll put some Treasures on the overhead projector, and flash the light on for just a second. Write how many Treasures you see on your Miniboard.

Do several "quick peeks," all for numbers from 1 to 5.

Have the children get their Miniboards ready. They should draw as they listen to your directions. Speak slowly and give the children a chance to finish drawing before moving on to the next part of the instruction.

Draw a house with a tree beside it. Draw 3 apples in the tree. Draw 2 birds in the tree. Now draw a kite in the tree.

How many things are in the tree?

Repeat using slightly different directions.

◇ 75 ◇ Count to Ten

Let's count to 10 together in some different voices.

Try these:

- *Use a silly voice.*  *1, 2, 3, 4, 5, 6, 7, 8, 9, 10.*

- *This time try a sad voice.*  *1, 2, 3, 4, 5, 6, 7, 8, 9, 10.*

- *Now let's do a mad voice.*  *1, 2, 3, 4, 5, 6, 7, 8, 9, 10.*

Count My Claps

*I'm going to clap. When I stop, tell me how many I did.
Ready? Listen carefully!*

Try various numbers of claps, from 1 to 10.

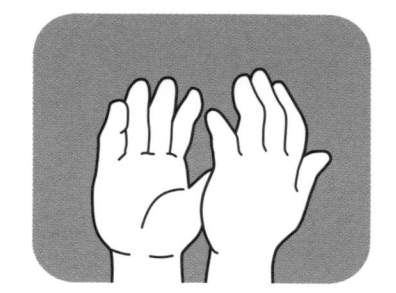

Make a List

I'll say a list of numbers. Write each number down on your Miniboard as I say it.

List several numbers from 1 to 9. At the end of each list, have the children show their Miniboards. Then have them clear their boards to get ready for the new list.

Shape Escape

Cut several shapes (circle, triangle, square, rectangle) out of construction paper. Then put them on the overhead projector.

Look at the shapes on the overhead projector. I'll turn out the light and take one away. When I turn the light back on, see if you can figure out which shape I took away. Draw the shape I took away on your Miniboard.

Play several rounds of the Shape Escape game.

79 ◆ Point It Out!

Hold up two Tactile Number Tiles, one in each hand, with your arms outstretched.

I'll say one of the numbers. Point to the one that I say.

Keep saying the number names in random order. You can speed it up when the children seem confident. For a trick, say a number name that's not shown!

After several rounds, change to two different number tiles and continue the game.

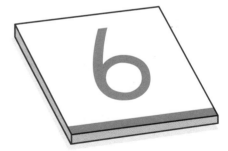

Take a Turn

Have the children sit in a large circle.

Let's count to 10 around the circle. One person starts us off with 1, then the next person in the circle says 2, and so on. When we get to 10, the next person in the circle starts us back at 1.

Count around the circle several times.

Now let's count to 7 around the circle.

81 ◇ If It's True...

I'm going to say something. Stand up if it's true. Stay seated if it's not true.

Make a variety of statements, some true and some not. After a few turns, the children might enjoy making the statements.

Try these:

• *I'm as tall as a house.*

• *There are more than 3 children in this room.*

• *I have 2 legs and 3 arms.*

Topic: Logical thinking   **Focus:** Identifying true and false statements

Name That Number

Use the Tactile Number Tiles, holding up one number tile at a time. Let the children practice naming numbers from 1 to 10.

I'll hold up a number tile. Say the number as soon as you know it.

Play many rounds of this game, increasing the pace as children gain confidence.

83 ◆ Long Sleeves, Short Sleeves

Everyone who's wearing long sleeves, stand up. Let's count these children as I point to each one. 1, 2, 3, 4, 5…. Now have a seat.

I'd like for everyone with short sleeves to stand up. Let's count these children.

Count many groups of children, using different attributes to determine the "standing up" group each time. Some attributes to try are: belts/no belts; tennis shoes/other shoes; and button shirts/pull-on shirts.

Topic: Counting **Focus:** Counting with 1-to-1 correspondence

MathLand™: Grade Kindergarten
© Creative Publications

Using the overhead projector, write these numbers on it: 3, 10, 1, 7, and 4.

Let's play Yes/No! Sign for "yes" if you see the number, sign for "no" if you don't. "Yes" if you see a 7 on the screen. "No" if you don't see a 5....

Give directions for several different sets of numbers. Vary the directions so that the children get to respond with both the signs.

If there is enough time, write a new set of numbers from 1 to 10 on the projector and play again.

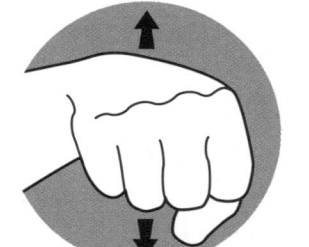

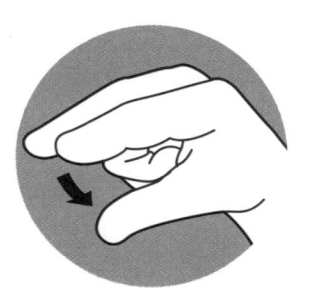

*American Sign Language (ASL) signs for Yes (top) and No (bottom).

⬦ 85 ⬦ **Treasure Count**

Place several small sets of Treasures out where the children can see them. Have the children count as you push each item aside.

Let's count the buttons together. I'll point as we count.
1, 2, 3, 4, 5. Now let's count the nuts and washers.

Make your way through each group. If time allows, put out several new sets to count.

Topic: Counting **Focus:** Counting with 1-to-1 correspondence MathLand™: Grade Kindergarten
© Creative Publications **85**

Number Detective

I'll write a number on the chalkboard, but I'll just draw it bit by bit. Try to guess what number it is before I finish writing the whole shape. Raise your hand when you think you know what it is.

Try the process with several numbers. Draw each number piece by piece, waiting to see if the children have guesses about what number you're writing. Add a piece at a time to the number, until many of the children have their hands raised. Then listen to their ideas about what the number is. Ask a child to come up and complete the number.

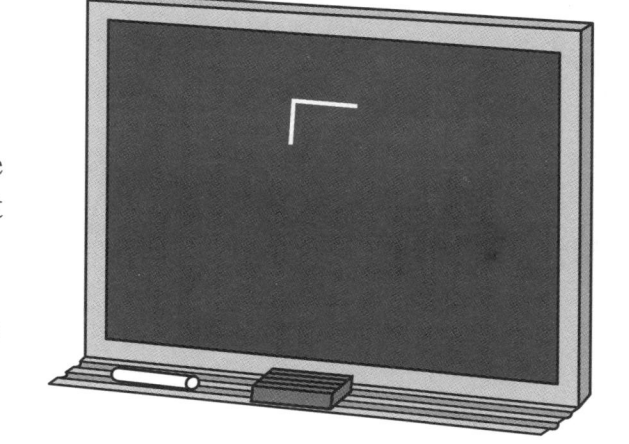

87 ◇ **Fast Fingers**

I'll hold up some fingers. As fast as you can, say how many I'm showing.

Keep the pace fast. As soon as the children have identified one set of fingers, put up a new group, using from 1 to 5 fingers each time. The goal here is instant recognition of groups of 1 to 5.

Plop, Plop

Have 10 Teddy Bear Counters and an empty juice can ready for this activity.

I'll plop the teddy bears into this can. Count the plops as we go. Start over at "1" every time I raise my hand.

Drop 1 teddy bear in, then raise your hand. Next, drop 2 teddy bears in before your hand goes up. Continue this with each number up to 10.

89   I Spy

Play a few rounds of the game I Spy with the children. Once children are familiar with the game, some might enjoy being the clue-giver.

I spy something square.
It's bigger than the garbage can.
You can see through it to the outside.
What is it? (a window)

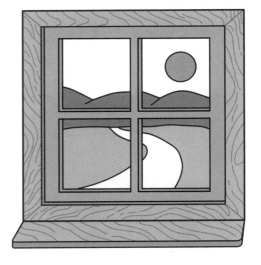

If It's True

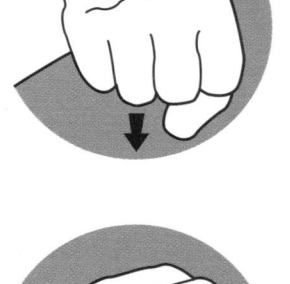

I'm going to say something. Sign for "yes" if it's true. Sign for "no" if it's not.

Make a variety of statements, some true and some not. After a few turns, the children might enjoy making the statements.

Try these:

• *The garbage can is under the desk.*

• *The door is open.*

• *It's raining out today.*

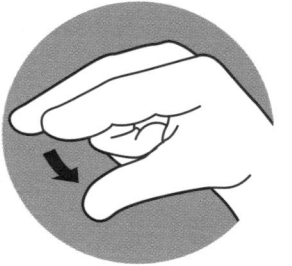

*American Sign Language (ASL) signs for Yes (top) and No (bottom).

91 ◆ **Riddles**

Tell the children several riddles and have them guess the answers. Here are some examples to use.

I'm red and wet.
You can dip a brush in me and
make a picture. (paint)

I'm flat and white.
I'm made from a tree.
You write on me. (paper)

Lead the children in this counting activity. Count to 10 over and over again. The first time through, count aloud. The second time through the sequence, mouth the numbers, but don't use voices.

Repeat the pattern, alternating between voiced and voiceless counting. Then try the activity again, choosing a new number.

93 ◆ Show Me

Can you write your numbers neatly? Show me. Write the numbers up to 5 on your Miniboard. Use your best writing.

Have the children show you their boards. Then have them clear their boards. Try the activity with several more series of numbers. *Show me 7, 8, and 9 in your best writing. How about 4, 5, and 6? Now let's try 2, 3, and 4.*

Sound Patterns

Have the children help you think of two animal sounds. Put the sounds together into a pattern, having the children join in when they know the pattern.

Try these:

• *Oink, oink, moo; oink, oink, moo; …*

• *Meow, woof; meow, woof; …*

• *Ssss, ssss, bzzz, bzzz; ssss, ssss, bzzz, bzzz; …*

Meow, woof.

95 ♦ **What Comes Next?**

Write this number pattern on the chalkboard: 1 2 3 1 2 3 1 2 ....

Let's read this pattern together. What comes next? Write it on your Miniboard. Show me your board.

Try several more number patterns, each time reading the pattern and having the children write the next element on their boards.

Try these:

• 1 1 5 1 1 5 1 1 ...

• 2 2 10 10 2 2 10 10 ...

• 3 4 5 3 4 5 3 4 ...

Top, Middle, or Bottom?

Write three numbers from 1 to 10 on the overhead projector in a vertical column.

Look at these numbers. I'll say a number name. You tell where that number is—top, middle, or bottom.

Say the number names in random order, pausing between each one to give all the children time to respond. Keep going until the children are quick and confident.

Now let's try three new numbers.

4
3
7

97   What's Next?

I'll write a few numbers in order on the chalkboard. Let's read them together. Now, write the number that comes next on your Miniboard.

Have the children show their boards after each time.

Try these:

- 1, 2, 3, 4
- 3, 4, 5, 6, 7
- 7, 8, 9

On Beyond Ten

I've got a secret number. Let's see if you can count to it.

Start a slow, steady rhythm by patting your knees. Have the children join in.

Now, let's count together. When you hit my secret number, I'll let you know!

Play several rounds of this game. Try these secret numbers: 11, 16, 18, and 13. When the children get to your number, stand up and applaud.

99 ◈ Write It Down!

I'll say some numbers. I'd like for you to write them on your Miniboard. Here we go: 10, 3, 5, and 9. Show me your board!

Let's go again. Ready? Clear your boards. Now write these numbers: 4, 8, 1, and 7.

Play several rounds of this game, using numbers from 1 to 10.

Topic: Number recognition **Focus:** Writing numerals
MathLand™: Grade Kindergarten
© Creative Publications

Hungry Bug

Have the children use their Miniboards. They can draw or tally on them to keep track while they listen to your story.

Listen to this story. Make a mark on your Miniboard for every thing the bug ate.

The other day, I watched a very hungry bug fly around my yard. She ate a leaf and a mosquito and a blade of grass and a speck of dirt. How many things did she eat?

Tell a few more "Hungry Bug" stories, always asking, *How many things did she eat?*

Topic: Number stories   **Focus:** Gathering data from a story

101 ◆ **Picnic Lunch**

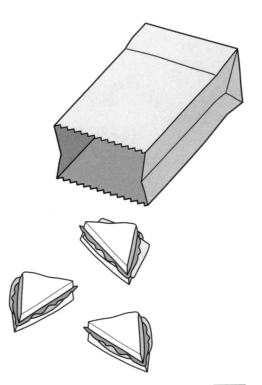

I'll tell you a story about a picnic lunch. Make a mark on your Miniboard for each kind of sandwich that you hear.

Willie was packing sandwiches for a picnic lunch. He packed a peanut butter and jelly sandwich, a tuna sandwich, and a chicken sandwich. How many sandwiches did Willie pack?

Tell several more "Picnic Lunch" stories, always asking, ***How many sandwiches did Willie pack?***

As children get more comfortable with the tally system of keeping track, you can make your stories a bit longer.

Who Can Count?

Who can count to 20? Show us!

Select volunteers to count for the group. Let everyone who wants to count have a turn.

Now let's all count to 20 together.

1, 2, 3, . . . 20.

Clap and Count

Count my claps. When I stop, write on your Miniboard the number that tells how many times I clapped.

Try random numbers of claps from 1 to 10.

Riddle Me This

Tell the children these riddles. Have them draw a picture of the answer on their Miniboards.

I am brown at the bottom and green at the top.
Birds live in me.
I have leaves. (a tree)

I'm red. I have a stem.
You eat me.
I'm crunchy.
I'm a kind of fruit. (an apple)

Try a few other riddles. Some children might enjoy making up the riddles.

105 ◇ **On Beyond 10**

Start a slow, steady clapping rhythm. Have the children join in.

Now, let's count while we clap. Keep the beat, and don't stop until I stand up.

Keep the count going beyond 10. Stand up at 15. Try the activity several more times, each time letting the count go higher.

1, 2, 3, . . . 20.

Topic: Counting   **Focus:** Rote counting beyond 10

Number Noises

Ask one child to name an animal sound. Possible responses could be woof, meow, and peep.

I'll say a number. All of you make the animal sound that many times. Let's try to stay together. Watch my hand for the beat. Ready?

Who has a different animal sound we could try?

Let's try a chicken sound. Squawk!

Make a Mark

I'll tell you a zoo story. Make a mark on your Miniboard for each one of the animals in the story.

At the zoo, I saw 2 giraffes. Next I walked by 3 lions. Then I passed by 1 polar bear and 2 penguins. How many animals did I see?

Try several more zoo stories if time permits.

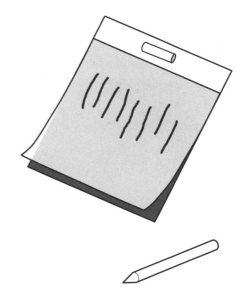

Listen and Count

Listen to my claps. When I stop clapping, everybody say how many claps you heard.

Try some numbers from 1 to 10.

6!

Quick Peeks

On the overhead projector, write three numbers while the overhead light is off. Turn the light on for just a few seconds. Have the children try to remember the numbers and write them on their Miniboards.

Get ready! You'll see three numbers on the screen. Try to remember what they are. Write them on your Miniboard.

Have the children show their Miniboards after each round.

Try several rounds of this memory game.

Clap and Count

Let's count to 7 again and again. Each time we count, let's start out counting silently and keep track with claps. I'll tell you how many claps to do. After the claps, let's count out loud the rest of the way to 7.

Try these:

• **3 claps**   *4, 5, 6, 7.*

• **5 claps**     *6, 7.*

• **4 claps**   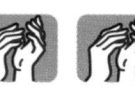     *5, 6, 7.*

A Fish Story

Have the children listen to the story. They may want to draw a picture to go with the story. They should write the answers on their Miniboards.

There were 7 fish swimming and playing under the waterfall. Then, 1 of their friends comes to join them. How many fish are now playing under the waterfall? Another fish comes along. How many are playing now?

Later, 1 fish has to leave to go to dinner. How many fish are left under the waterfall?

Plop, Plop

Show the children some LinkerCubes and an empty juice can.

I'll drop some cubes into the can. Count with me as each one plops into the can.

Drop the cubes slowly into the can. Continue so that the count goes beyond 10. Empty the can and try the activity again, each time counting higher than the last round.

113 Faster and Faster

On the overhead projector, write these numbers: 10, 7, 6, 0, and 3.

When I point to each number, say it out loud. Remember, I like to speed up my pointing because you're so good at this!

Point from number to number in random order. When the children feel confident with the number names, begin pointing from one to the other faster and faster.

Now let's try some new numbers.

Write a Number...

Have the children get their Miniboards out. They should show you their boards after each instruction, and then clear their boards to prepare for the next instruction.

Try these:

- **Write a number that's greater than 5.**

- **Now write two numbers that are less than 8.**

- **Write three numbers that you say in a row when you're counting.**

115 ◆ How Many?

Have the children get their Miniboards ready. Say a number and have the children draw that many circles. They should show you their boards after each number, and then clear their boards to prepare for the next number.

I'll say a number. You draw that many circles on your board.

Try some numbers from 1 to 10. Then add zero to your list. Talk with the children about the meaning of zero.

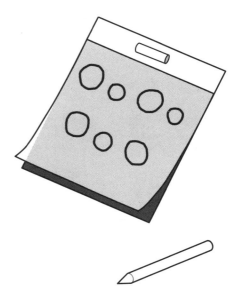

I'll clap some rhythms for you. Listen carefully. When I stop and say "GO" repeat what you heard. Ready? Here are the first claps:

Fast, fast, slow, slow; fast, fast, slow, slow; …

Echoes…ready, GO!

Now try some other long and short clapping rhythms. Move progressively from shorter patterns to longer ones. Repeat any rhythms that seem difficult for the children.

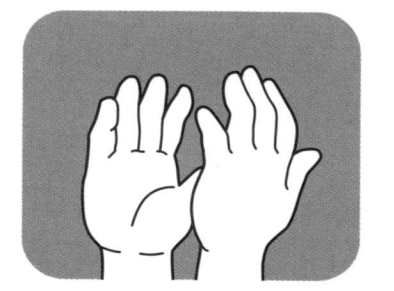

Write It Down!

Have the children get out their Miniboards.

I'll say some numbers one at a time. Write each one on your Miniboard as I say it. Ready? 5, 3, 2, 9, 0, 6. Now, show me your boards.

Try this activity several times, giving a different list of numbers each time. Include zero in several of your lists, as well as any numbers with which the children seem to be having difficulty.

Topic: Number recognition

Focus: Writing numerals

MathLand™: Grade Kindergarten
© Creative Publications

Count On

Miniboards ready? I'll say a number and then clap my hands, saying the next numbers silently to myself. When I stop, write my last number on your board.

Start with numbers from 1 to 9, adding several claps to each number. For a challenge, use larger numbers and more claps.

Try these:

- *3*

- *1*

- *8*

119 Estimate

Place 5 to 10 LinkerCubes on the overhead projector.
Leave the light off.

I'll flash the overhead light on and off. You'll see some cubes on the screen. When the light goes off, make a guess about how many there were. Write your guess on your Miniboard.

Play several rounds of this estimation game. After each estimate, have the children help you count to see how many cubes were actually shown.

Some young children are reluctant to make estimates and want all of their guesses to be perfect. You can help them by making the Miniboard estimates private. The children can write down their guess, but they don't have to show their boards.

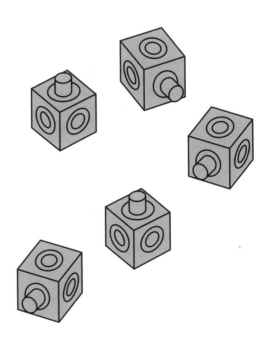

I'll stamp my foot. Count the stamps and write how many on your Miniboard.

Stamp your foot, using numbers from 1 to 10. Repeat the activity a number of times.

Watch as I draw a shape on the overhead projector.
When I raise my hand, let's say the name of the shape
together.

One at a time, draw different shapes (square, equilateral
triangle, circle, rectangle, right triangle) on the overhead
projector. Have the children name each shape (square,
triangle, circle, rectangle, triangle) as you draw it.

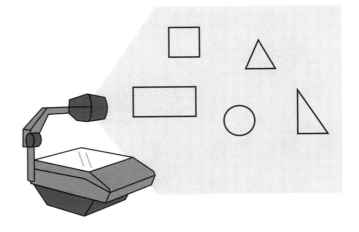

Number Detective

I'll give you some clues. Try to guess which number I'm talking about. Write the answer on your Miniboard.

Try some number riddles like the following. Make up some of your own or have the children make up some riddles.

My number is less than 5.
It isn't 3.
It's the shape of a circle.
What's my number? (0)

My number is greater than 4.
It's less than 9.
It rhymes with "Kevin."
What's my number? (7)

Count On

I'll say a number and then clap my hands, saying the next numbers silently to myself. When I stop, write my ending number on your Miniboard.

Try these:

- 7

- 15

- 10

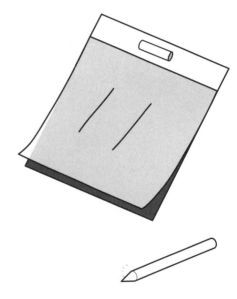

How High?

Let's count together for twenty seconds. I'll say STOP when our time is up. We'll see how high we can get. Stay together, use my voice as your guide. Ready, GO….

Try this several times, increasing the pace a little each time.

◈ 125 ◈   **Monster Story**

Tell the children a monster story. Have them draw pictures on their Miniboards to help them remember the story.

There was a monster who loved to collect shapes. He got a circle, 2 squares, a triangle, another circle, 1 more square, and a heart.

How many circles does he have? How many squares? Which things does he have only one of? How many shapes did he collect in all?

Try one or two more monster stories as time permits.

Alike and Different

I'll name two or three objects. Raise your hand if you can name something they have in common. After calling on several children, say, *Raise your hand if you can name one way that they are different.*

Try these:

- *Basketball, balloon, and an orange*

- *Sink and a bucket*

- *Fish, boat, and a rubber ducky*

◆ 127 ◆ Draw This

I'll name a shape. Draw it on your Miniboard.

Name one shape at a time, having the children show their boards when they've drawn each one. Have the children clear their boards before you name the next shape.

Try these:

• ***Square***

• ***Circle***

• ***Triangle***

For a challenge, try a heart and a star.

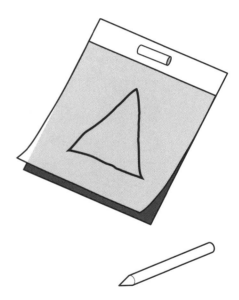

Topic: Geometry   **Focus:** Drawing shapes   MathLand™: Grade Kindergarten
© Creative Publications   **127**

Have the children get their Miniboards ready. *I'm going to tell an animal story. You can keep track of the number of animals in the story with tally marks.*

I went to the zoo yesterday. I saw a lion, a giraffe, and a zebra. How many animals did I see? Write the number on your board.

Here's a new story. I went to the zoo. I saw a lioness and her baby cub. How many animals did I see?

Tell one or two more "Zoo Stories" to the children. After each story, ask, *How many animals did I see?*

129 Count 'Em Up

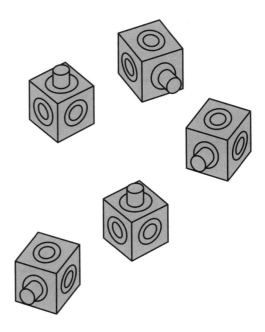

Are your Miniboards ready? I'll put some LinkerCubes on the overhead projector. Each time I turn the light on, write the number that tells how many cubes you see. Keep a list on your board of all the numbers you count.

Start with 5 cubes. Show each cube configuration and have the children write that number on their Miniboard lists. Between configurations, turn the light off, and add or take away one or two cubes before displaying the new configuration.

Topic: Mental math   **Focus:** Visualizing numbers   MathLand™: Grade Kindergarten
© Creative Publications   **129**

Fifty Is Nifty

Let's count together to 50. Follow my voice so that we stay together. 1, 2, 3, … 50!

If you like, try counting to 50 while clapping, or stomping, or hopping.

46, 47, 48, 49, 50!

Let's Estimate!

I'm going to flash the overhead projector light on for just a few seconds. You'll see some LinkerCubes, but probably won't have time to count them.

Write a number on your Miniboard that you think is pretty close to the number of cubes. Then we'll turn the light back on and count to check how close our estimates were.

Use 5 to 10 cubes each time you play, turning the light on for just a few seconds. Have the children write their estimates on their boards. Then turn the light back on, counting the cubes as a group.

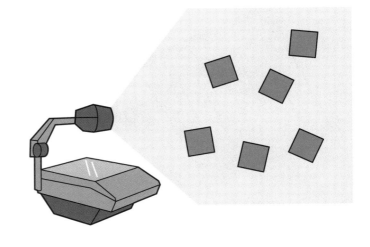

Have the children use their Miniboards to keep track of your story if they wish.

At my house, there was a terrible mess. I picked up a coat, a hat, a book, the newspaper, and a plate.

How many things did I pick up? How many things to read did I pick up? How many things to wear?

Tell one or two more "It Was a Mess!" stories. Some of the children may like to try telling one as well.

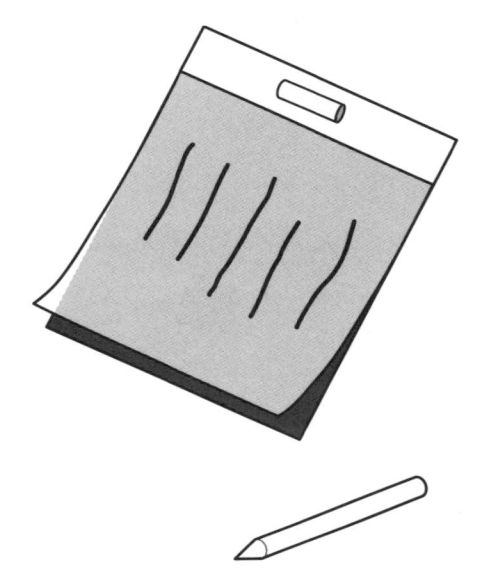

Let's Count!

*Let's count together. Start at **1**, and keep going until I raise my hand.*

Try this several times, stopping the counting at various numbers from 70 to 100.

1, 2, 3, ...80.

Get your Miniboards ready! Follow my directions about what to draw.

Draw a square in the middle of your board. Draw a circle inside the square. Now draw a triangle above the square. Make the circle into a "smiley" face.

Show me your boards!

135 ◆ **What Comes Next?**

I'll say a number. On your Miniboard write the number that comes next. Ready? Here's the number—7. What comes next? The children write 8 on their boards.

Try this several times, using numbers from 0 to 9. Have the children show you their Miniboards after each "What Comes Next?" question.

Topic: Sequencing numbers   **Focus:** Writing the next number

MathLand™: Grade Kindergarten
© Creative Publications

Sizing Up

Have the children get their Miniboards ready.

Draw three circles on your board. Make one small, one medium-sized, and one large.

Have the children show their boards. Then have them clear their boards in preparation for your next instruction. Try the activity again with a different shape (squares, triangles, rectangles, hearts, stars).

Topic: Measurement   **Focus:** Size comparisons

Your Best Writing

I'll say three numbers. Write each one on your Miniboard in your very neatest writing.

Use numbers from 0 to 10. Have the children show their boards after each series of numbers. Then have them clear their boards to prepare for the next series.

Topic: Number recognition   **Focus:** Writing numerals

Cut out several shapes (square, triangle, circle, rectangle, star, and heart) from construction paper. On the overhead projector stage arrange two or three of the shapes at a time.

Look at the shapes on the screen. Sign for Yes if you see the shape I ask about. Sign for No if you don't. Is there a square? How about a diamond? Is there a heart?

After several questions, project a different group of shapes on the screen. Ask questions about each group of shapes.

Whisper, SHOUT

Try counting by twos with your class in this way. Count to 20 or 30 each time.

Let's count together out loud with a "Whisper, SHOUT" pattern. We'll count, taking turns whispering, then shouting the numbers. Ready? One, TWO, three, FOUR, five, SIX….

Now, let's try starting with a different number. How about 7? Count with me. Are you ready? Seven, EIGHT, nine, TEN, eleven, TWELVE….

Topic: Counting

Focus: Skip counting by twos

140 Memory Test

I'm going to say three numbers. Listen very carefully, then try to remember all three of them and write them down on your Miniboard. Ready?

For each round, say three numbers from 0 to 10. Have the class show their boards each time.

Try these:

• *5, 8, 0*

• *3, 7, 1*

• *2, 3, 4*

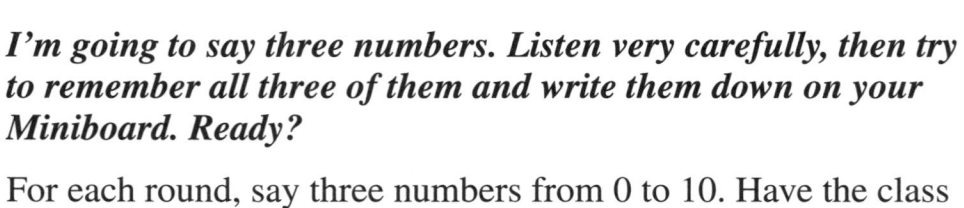

◇ 141 ◇ **Number Riddles**

Here are some riddles for you. I'll give you a little hint—the answers are numbers! Write the answer to each riddle on your Miniboard.

It's more than 1. It's less than 3.
It's between 1 and 3. (2)

This number is bigger than 5.
It's smaller than 10.
It's made out of 2 circles. (8)

Tell a few more number riddles, then let the children try inventing some.

Miniboards ready? Draw three lines on your board. Make two of the lines the same length, and make one shorter.

Have the children show their boards after each request, and then clear the boards in preparation for the next instruction.

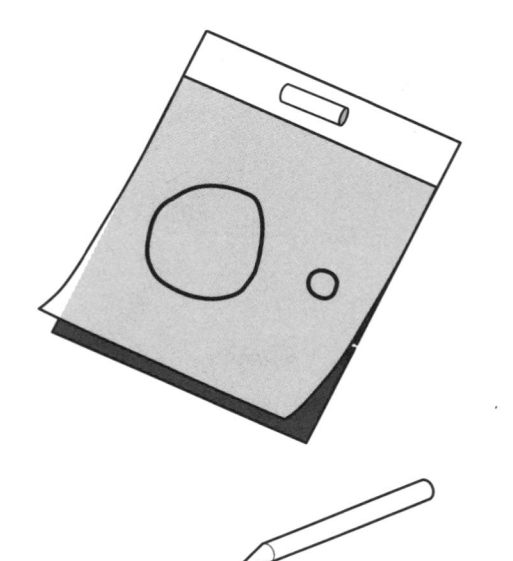

Try these:

• *Draw a big circle and a little circle.*

• *Can you draw a tall tree next to a short tree?*

• *Show me a small square, a medium square, and a large square.*

Count On

I'll say a number and then clap my hands, saying the next numbers silently to myself. When I stop, write my ending number on your Miniboard.

Try these:

• *10*

• *16*

• *20*

What Comes Before?

I'll say a number. On your Miniboard write the number that comes just before it.

Try this several times, using numbers from 1 to 10.

Lengthy Lines

Miniboards ready? Let's draw some lines today.

Try these:

- *Draw a line on your board that's shorter than your pinkie finger.*

- *Now draw one that's longer than your pinkie finger.*

- *How about one that's the same length as your pinkie finger?*

Who Can Count?

Who can count to 50? Show us!

Select volunteers to count for the group. Let everyone who wants to count have a turn.

Now let's all count to 50 together.

1, 2, 3, . . . 50!

147 ◇ Show Me

Can you write all of the numbers from 1 to 10? Show me on your Miniboard.

Now, clear your board and only show me the numbers from 1 to 5.

See if you can show me only number 6 and number 3.

Topic: Number recognition   **Focus:** Writing numerals

Point It Out!

On the chalkboard draw three vertical lines, separated by a large amount of space. One should be longer than the others, one shorter, and one in between.

I'll say "longer," "shorter," or "middle-sized." Point to the line on the board that matches my words. Are you ready? Shorter, longer, middle-sized. Repeat using a different order.

Set a quick pace, having the children point from one line to the other as soon as you've indicated the line. After a while draw three new lines, rearranging the order of the line lengths, and try the activity again.

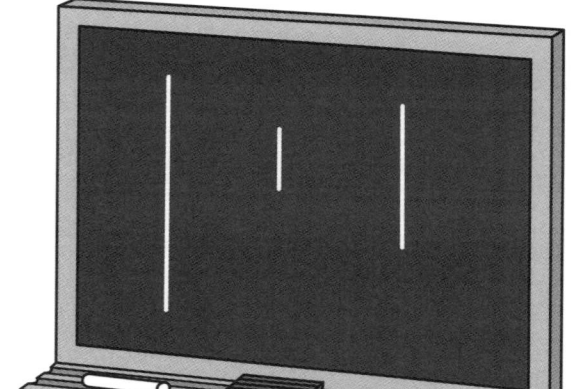

149 > Write a Number...

Have the class get their Miniboards ready. They should show their boards between each direction, and then clear the boards to prepare for the next instruction.

Try these:

- **Write a number that's less than 10.**

- **Write a number that's more than 3.**

- **Write the number that's 1 more than 5.**

What's My Number?

Here are some number riddles for you.

I'm thinking of a number.
It's between 1 and 7.
It comes after 5.
It's not 7.
What's my number? (6)

I'm thinking of a number.
It's made with straight lines.
It starts with the "ssss" sound.
It's not 6.
What's my number? (7)

Try some more number riddles with the class.

151   Count 'Em Up

Are your Miniboards ready? I'll put some LinkerCubes on the overhead projector. Each time I turn the light on, write the number that tells how many cubes you see. Keep a list on your board of all the numbers you count.

Start this activity with 5 cubes. Show each cube configuration and have the children write that number on their Miniboard list. Between configurations, turn the projector light off. Add or take away one or two cubes before displaying the new configuration to the class.

---

100 Count

Let's count all the way to 100. Do you think we can do it? Let's try! 1, 2, 3, ... 100!

Count aloud with the group, helping them keep the pace steady.

1, 2, 3, . . .100!

153 Two by Two

How many hands do you think we have in our classroom today? Let's count! We'll count the first hand in whispery voices, and the next one in loud voices. Everyone put your hands out in front of you.

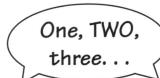

One, TWO, three. . .

Go around the circle, touching hands as you count. Help the children keep up the "whisper, SHOUT, whisper, SHOUT" pattern. *Ready? One, TWO, three, FOUR, five, SIX …. How many hands did we count?*

Now let's try counting shoes. How many do you think there will be? Use a similar procedure to count the shoes, using loud voices for every other number.

Try counting other things (eyes, ears, knees) in the class that come in twos.

What's Next?

I'll write some numbers in order on the overhead projector.
When I stop, you write the next number on your Miniboard.

Write a short series of numbers on the overhead projector. The children should write the next number in the sequence on their Miniboards. Have the children show their boards after each series of numbers.

Try these:

• 1, 2, 3, 4, 5

• 7, 8, 9

• 4, 5, 6, 7

1, 2, 3, 4, 5

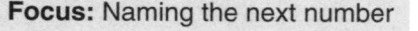

Plop, Plop

Show the children some Teddy Bear Counters and an empty plastic container. ***Let's count together as I drop each teddy bear into the container.*** Drop the teddy bears slowly into the container. Be sure you continue so that the count goes beyond 20 or 30.

Empty the plastic container and try the activity again, each time counting higher than the last round.

156 Listen Closely!

It's a Miniboard day! Are you ready? I'll give you some instructions. Let's see how well you can remember them.

Wait until I've finished giving the instructions before you start drawing. Ready? Draw a square with a triangle above it. Let's see your boards. Clear your boards and let's go again!

Try these:

* *Draw two triangles, a square, and a circle.*

* *Draw a triangle, then draw a square that's smaller than the triangle.*

* *Draw a big square, a little square, and a big circle.*

Topic: Auditory memory   **Focus:** Following directions   MathLand™: Grade Kindergarten
© Creative Publications   **156**

Count 'Em Up

On the overhead projector write some numbers from 1 to 10 in random spaces. Repeat some of the numbers several times.

Look at these numbers. How many twos do you see? How many fives are there? How many eights? How many ones?

Bigger and Smaller

Can you think of something that is bigger than you are? Draw a picture of it on your Miniboard. Have the children show their Miniboards. Let them tell about their drawings.

Clear your boards. Now draw a picture of something that's smaller than you are. Let's see what kinds of things you drew this time.

Topic: Measurement

Focus: Comparing size

159 ◆ Countdown

Practice counting backward with the children. Each time, start from a different number, always counting back down to zero.

Try these:

• *Let's count backward from 10 to zero.*

• *Let's count backward from 7 to zero.*

• *Let's count backward from 20 to zero.*

10, 9, 8, . . . 0!

Memory Test

Here's a Miniboard game to stretch your memory. Write three numbers from 1 to 10 on the overhead projector. Then turn the projector light on to show the numbers. *Look closely now. Try to remember my numbers.*

Turn the projector light off and have the children write the numbers they remember seeing on their Miniboards.

7 9
4

Clap and Count

Let's count to 100. We'll clap as we count, one clap for each number. Clap at a slow, steady pace as the counting continues.

Try other actions while counting to 100, such as stamping, snapping, and patting.

Counting Back

It's a Miniboard day! I'll count backward for a bit. When I stop, write the number that should be next. Ready? 10, 9, 8, 7, 6, 5. What comes next?

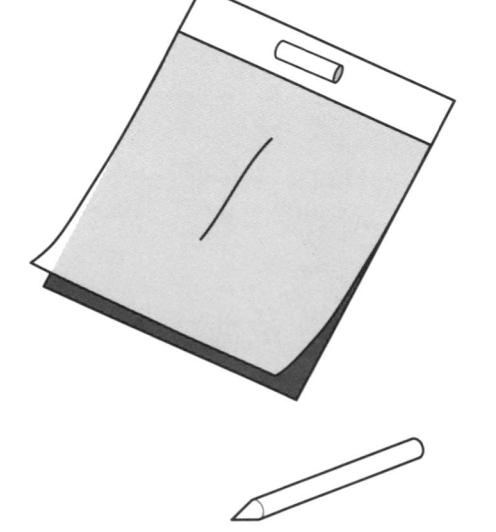

Try these:

• *6, 5, 4, 3, 2, ...*   ***What comes next?***

• *9, 8, 7, ...*   ***What comes next?***

• *3, 2, 1, ...*   ***What comes next?***

163 Yes/No

Arrange a small number of Treasures (1 to 5) on the overhead projector. Turn the overhead light off. ***I'll turn the overhead light on for just a second, then I'll say a number. If you see the same number of Treasures as the number I said, sign for "yes". If I said a different number from the number of Treasures you see, sign for "no".***

Change the number of Treasures, and try the activity again. Show each group of Treasures for just two or three seconds, working toward quick recognition of groups of 1 to 5.

*American Sign Language (ASL) signs for Yes (top) and No (bottom).

On the Nose

I'm thinking of a number from 1 to 10. Let's see if you can guess what it is. Call on individual children to guess a number. After each guess, say ***higher*** or ***lower.*** Continue until the correct number is guessed. Then say, ***On the nose!***

Play several rounds of the game.

Higher!

Write Two Numbers...

Get your Miniboards ready! Write two numbers you know that are more than 7. Show me your board.

Try these:

• **Write two numbers you know that are less than 5.**

• **Write two numbers you know that are more than 3.**

• **Write two numbers you know that are less than 10.**

Let's count! When I raise my arms, stop counting.

Try these:

 Let's start at 20.

 20, 21, 22, 23, 24, 25, … 35.

 Now let's start at 30.

30, 31, 32, 33, 34, 35, … 45.

 Let's start at 40.

40, 41, 42, 43, 44, 45, … 55.

167 Which Is More?

On the chalkboard write the numbers from 0 to 10 in random order. Point to two numbers at a time, and have the children respond aloud, telling which number is greater.

I'll point to two of these numbers. Which one is more? How about these two? Which one is more? Now try these two.

Keep the pace fast. As soon as the children respond to one pair of numbers, quickly point to the next two.

Write the numbers from 0 to 10 on the chalkboard in random order. Point to two numbers at a time, and have the children respond aloud, telling which number is less.

I'll point to two of these numbers. Which one is smaller? How about these two? Which one is less? Now try these two.

Keep the pace fast. As soon as the children respond to one pair of numbers, quickly point to the next two.

5!

What Comes Next?

I'm going to say a number. You say the number that comes next. We'll try some big numbers, too. Think carefully. Here we go!

Say random numbers, focusing on those from 1 to 10 at first, and then mixing in some larger numbers.

Try these:

- *7*  8

- *4*  5

- *14*  15

Topic: Sequencing numbers   **Focus:** Naming the next number   MathLand™: Grade Kindergarten © Creative Publications   169

Count and Kick

Have the children join you to form a large circle. *Stand in a circle and put an arm around the shoulder of the person on each side of you.* Show the children how to kick with alternating legs: right leg, then left; right leg, then left.

Now let's count while we kick. Let's see how high we can get. Do you think we can count past 100?